SAIL AWAY

Donald Crews

Scholastic Inc.

New York Toronto London Auckland Sydney

To the Seabiscuit,
captain and crew,
and to being here
to tell this tale

The full-color illustrations were created
with Dr. Martin's Concentrated Water Colors
applied with brush and airbrush.

ISBN 0-590-85911-0

Copyright © 1995 by Donald Crews.
All rights reserved. Published by Scholastic Inc., 555 Broadway,
New York, NY 10012, by arrangement with Greenwillow Books,
a division of William Morrow & Company, Inc.

12 11 10 9 8 7 6 5 4 3 2 1   6 7 8 9/9 0 1/0

Printed in the U.S.A.   14

First Scholastic printing, April 1996

A perfect
day for
sailing.

**We row the dinghy
out to our sailboat.**

**Everything ready,
we motor from our mooring.**
p u t t . . . p u t t . . . p u t t . . .

putt...putt...putt...
Under the bridge.
putt...putt...putt...

p u t t . . . p u t t . . . p u t t . . .
**Past the lighthouse.
Motor off.** *p u t t . . .* **Sails up . . .**

Wind's up...

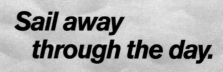

Sail away through the day.

**Sailing, sailing.
Clear skies turn
cloudy and gray.**

**Gray skies darken.
Seas swell.**

Darker skies,
higher seas...
Angry
seas.
"Shorten sails!"

Sails down, we turn for home.

**Calm again at last.
The sun is setting
as we motor toward port.**
p u t t . . . p u t t . . . p u t t . . .

putt...putt...putt...
Past the lighthouse.
putt...putt...putt...

putt...putt...putt...
Under the bridge.
putt...putt...putt...

Moored!